FESTIVE FUN

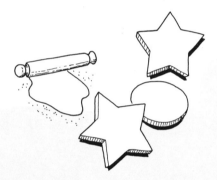

Angela Ludlow

Illustrations by
Linda Francis

A LION BOOK

Oxford · Batavia · Sydney

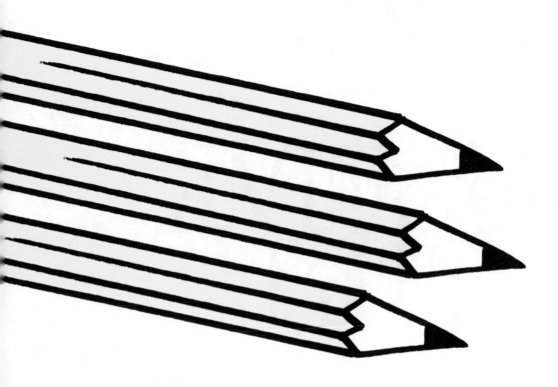

Published by
Lion Publishing plc
Sandy Lane West, Oxford, England
ISBN 0 7459 1484 5
Albatross Books Pty Ltd
PO Box 320, Sutherland, NSW 2232, Australia
ISBN 0 7324 0192 5

First edition 1992

Reprinted 1993

Printed and bound in Thailand

Contents

Thinking about Easter

You have probably heard people say that they are going to give something up for Lent - often people give up sweets or special treats. But have you ever wondered why? We have to go back nearly 2000 years to the time of Jesus' life on earth to discover the answer.

From school or home or church most of us know something of the story of Jesus' birth in Bethlehem. (You can refresh your memory by reading all about it in the Christmas section of this book.) But what happened after that? What happened when Jesus grew up? That's what we need to know if we are to understand what Lent is all about.

The origins of Lent

Even as a baby Jesus was special: the Bible says he was God's own son, sent into the world for a very special reason. But no one knew anything about that until Jesus was about thirty, when he began to travel the land telling people about God.

To prepare for this work, Jesus went away by himself into the desert for forty days to be alone and to discover what God wanted him to do. God's enemy, Satan (sometimes known as the devil), waited till Jesus was hungry and thirsty, and then tried to make him disobey God. But Jesus refused to give in to Satan's suggestions, and in the end he went away.

The Christian church remembers this time in the forty days before Easter - the period we call Lent.

In the Middle Ages, Lent was a time of fasting when people went without such foods as meat, eggs and cream.

In many countries the day before Lent is called 'Mardi Gras' or 'Fat Tuesday' and in other countries Pancake Day or Shrove Tuesday. Traditionally this was the day when people used up all the fats in the house by making pancakes and enjoying the kinds of foods they would have to go without until Easter. Christians today may give things up in order to give to others. They also try to spend more time in prayer and Bible study - learning and thinking about God.

Pancakes

WHAT YOU NEED

★ bowl

★ fork or whisk

★ frying pan

★ spatula

★ plate

★ 100g/4oz self-raising flour

★ pinch of salt

★ 1 egg

★ about 300ml/½ pint milk

★ vegetable oil

★ butter or lemon juice and sugar or syrup

1. Mix the flour and salt in the bowl. Make a well in the centre of the mixture and break the egg into it. Stir carefully with the fork or whisk to mix in the flour.

2. When the mixture in the centre is thick and creamy, begin adding milk and stir in more flour from around the sides of the bowl. Continue adding milk until the mixture is like thin cream.

3. Ask a grown-up to heat a little oil in a frying pan and then wipe it to leave the surface just lightly oiled. Add a spoonful of pancake mix and cook on a gentle heat till the bubbles on the surface burst. Use a spatula to flip the pancake over and cook for a minute or two on the other side.

Stack your pancakes on a plate and keep them in a warm place until all the mixture is cooked.

Serve with a little butter or lemon, with sugar or syrup.

If your frying pan is not too hot or heavy, you may like to try tossing your pancakes. When you have got one side cooked, jiggle the pan to make sure the pancake is loose, and then jerk the pan upwards to toss the pancake over. The trick is to catch it again!

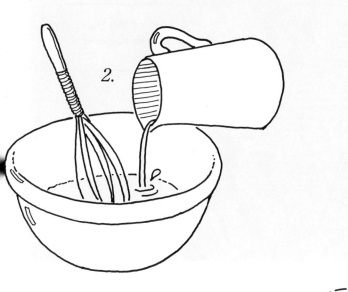

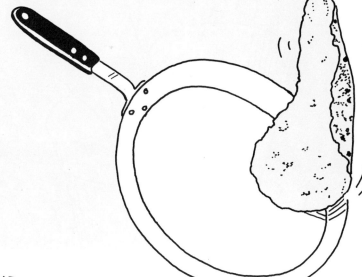

New Life

If it is springtime in your country, you will see signs of new life in the natural world. Leaves, flowers and grasses will begin to show. Birds will begin building their nests, in which to lay eggs and raise their chicks.

Wherever you live, here are two activities that you could start ahead of time for Easter.

Grow a plant

A seed looks so dull and dead. When you bury it in the soil, you might think you are saying goodbye to it for ever. But if you plant a seed in the right conditions it will grow into a new plant.

WHAT YOU NEED

★ plant pot or any small plastic pot with a hole poked through the bottom

★ saucer

★ soil

★ paper large enough to cover the pot

★ plastic wrap

★ two or three plant seeds

1. Fill the plant pot about three-quarters full with soil. Place it on the saucer. Gently water the soil so that it is quite moist. Extra water will run through into the saucer.

2. Drop the seeds in the pot, and cover lightly with a little more soil.

3. Cover the pot with a piece of paper, and then with a piece of plastic wrap. Place the pot on a light window-sill, but not one that gets too much sun.

4. Check your pot every two or three days. In a little while, you will see shoots appearing. As soon as you do, take off the paper and the plastic wrap and let the plants grow in the light.

If your plants do well, decide which shoot is the strongest and nip off the others. Grow your plant to full size by keeping the soil moist and the plant in a well-lit place.

Why not give your plant as a gift on Easter day?

Egg-shaped gifts

Eggs are another symbol of new life. From the outside they look as lifeless as stone, yet within them a new creature is slowly developing. When it is ready, the baby creature chips its way out.

In many countries eggs are painted or dyed as Easter gifts. Some countries in Eastern Europe have their own traditions for decorating eggs. In Poland, people traditionally use geometric designs. In Hungary, it is the custom to paint red flowers on a white background. In Yugoslavia the eggs may be marked with the letters XV, which stand for "Christos vaskrese" or "Christ is risen".

Wrap small gifts for your family and friends in these egg-shaped papier maché cases. They will be amazed at how you got the gifts inside!

WHAT YOU NEED

★ balloon for each shape that you want to make

★ strips of torn-up paper, such as newspaper

★ wallpaper paste

★ small gifts to put in each balloon

★ string

★ scissors

★ poster paints and brushes

★ coloured stickers

1. Put a gift inside each balloon. Blow each balloon up till it is the size of a large egg. Tie it shut, leaving a length of string hanging.

2. Coat the strips of paper in wallpaper paste and cover the balloon evenly with them. Hang up to dry.

3. Each day for five days, add another layer of pasted paper. When the papier maché is dry, snip off the top of the balloon. Add a few pieces of pasted paper to cover the gap.

4. Paint your papier maché eggs in bright colours. When the paint is dry, decorate them with stickers.

Gifts for your egg

wrapped sweets

coins

pencil sharpener

jewellery, buttons or beads

key ring

marbles

1.

2.

3.

4.

7

A Day for Mothers

In days gone by, the fourth Sunday of Lent was a time when people would go to worship in the main church of their parish, called the mother church. Young people who worked as servants in other people's households were given that day off to go to their home church. Often they would bring a cake they had baked or flowers they had picked as a gift for their mother. The day became a family celebration: Mothering Sunday.

More recently, an American woman called Anna Jarvis suggested that one day each year be set aside specially for mothers. The idea appealed to other people. The day chosen was a Sunday in May. This became Mother's Day. Whatever the date, it is good to find a special way to say "thank you" to our mothers.

A breakfast tray

Make a special paper traycloth and napkin on which to take your mother her favourite breakfast.

WHAT YOU NEED

★ serving tray

★ green paper, large enough to fit the tray, plus some extra

★ square of coloured paper, about 60cm by 60cm

★ scissors

★ compasses and pencil, or a round plate

★ glue

★ marker pens

1. Cut a piece of green paper to fit neatly inside the tray. Set this aside.

2. Using the compasses or a plate, draw a semi-circle on green paper, with a diameter of about 25cm. Cut it out, fold into a cone and glue in place.

3. Draw a flower shape as large as you can on your coloured paper and cut it out. Use marker pens to decorate the flower with stamens.

4. Fold the flower, decorated side inwards, into four. Roll gently into a cone shape and place in the green cone, so it looks like a flower bud.

5. Draw small flowers on the remaining coloured paper and decorate them in a similar way. Cut them out and glue them in a pretty arrangement around the green paper covering the tray.

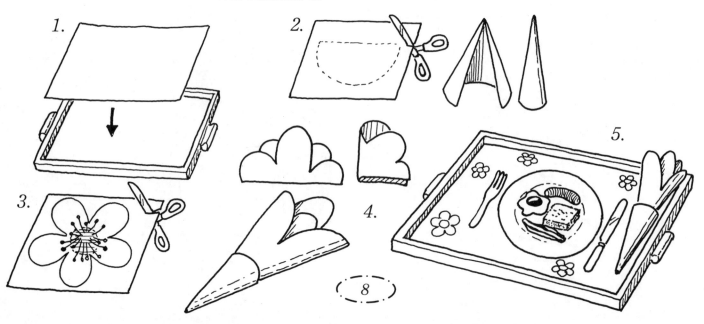

Flower card

Flowers are a traditional gift on Mother's Day. This flower card comes on its own stem and could be added to a vase of real flowers.

WHAT YOU NEED

★ paper, about 5cm by 50cm

★ paint

★ pen

★ sticky tape

★ glue

★ two ice lolly sticks

1. Paint one side of the paper. Use yellow along the lower long edge, and a flower colour for the rest.

2. Turn the card over and write a message on the top edge.

3. Fold the paper concertina-fashion. Tape the lower edge (the yellow one) shut with a piece of sticky tape, and keep the rest of the paper folded.

4. Paint the ice lolly sticks green. Glue one on each end of the paper concertina. They should not reach quite into the yellow section, and they should jut out the other side.

5. Present the card closed. You open it by pulling the sticks round to meet each other, so that the paper flower opens like a fan.

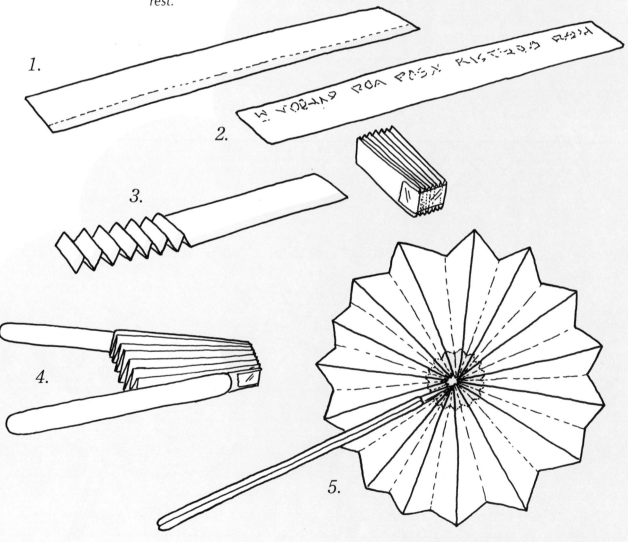

Gifts for Mother

Carnation posy

In some countries it is traditional for people to wear a white carnation in honour of their mothers.

WHAT YOU NEED

★ three small white tissues

★ small piece of florist's wire, or a long pipecleaner

★ small piece of green paper

★ paper doily

★ glue

★ sharp scissors

1. Place three small tissues on top of each other. Fold them together concertina-fashion. Fold in half.

2. Twist the wire tightly around the base. Trim round the top with scissors and gently ease out the tissues, pulling them gently to form the petals of the flower.

3. Cut leaf shapes from the green paper and glue them around the centre of the doily.

4. Insert the flower wire through the centre of the doily. Fold the wire to leave just a short handle, and twist the rest around the base of the posy to hold it in position.

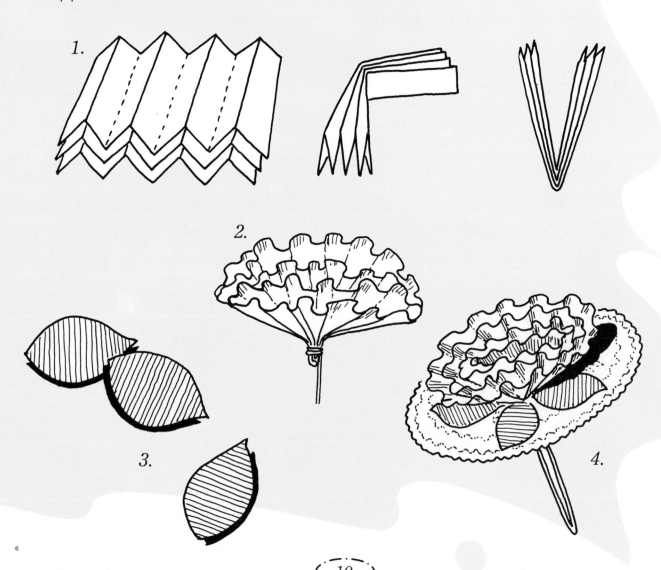

Organizer boxes

While your mother is relaxing on Mother's Day, you could make some organizer boxes for any of your things that are all too often left lying about!

WHAT YOU NEED

★ empty packages, in a variety of sizes

★ shallow box

★ paint

★ glue

1. Arrange the empty packages in the cardboard box, to create lots of different compartments to hold your things.

2. Take them out and paint the outside of the box and the packages. Let them dry.

3. Glue the base of each package and put it in its place in the box.

The useful bit, of course, is organizing your belongings so that they aren't scattered about, and even you can find them!

1.

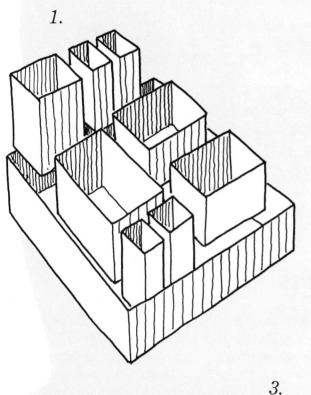

2.

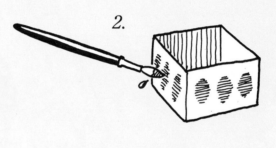

3.

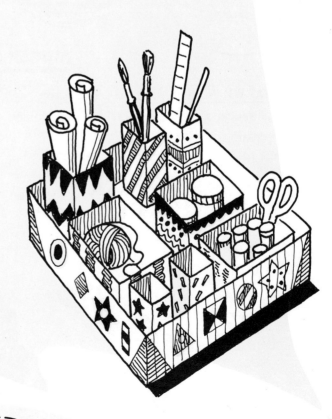

Edible Gifts

Coconut delights

WHAT YOU NEED

★ bowl
★ mixing spoon
★ rolling pin
★ 100g/4oz cream cheese
★ 1 dessertspoon honey
★ 100g/4oz digestive biscuits
★ desiccated coconut

1. Mix the cream cheese and honey together in a bowl until smooth. You may find adding a few drops of milk will help you make a creamy mixture more easily.

2. Put the biscuits in another bowl and crush with a rolling pin.

3. Mix the cheese and biscuit crumbs together.

4. Make small balls of the mixture and roll each one in the coconut.

5. Leave to set in the refrigerator.

Eat these within two days of making them.

Muesli candies

WHAT YOU NEED

★ small saucepan
★ ice cream scoop or large spoon
★ paper cases

★ 100g/4oz butter
★ 4 tablespoons golden syrup
★ 2 tablespoons unsweetened cocoa powder
★ 200g/8oz muesli

1. Melt the butter and syrup in a saucepan with the cocoa, and bring to the boil.

2. Take the pan off the heat and stir in the cereal.

3. Press the mixture into a small ice cream scoop or large spoon to make round heaps. Place one in each paper case and leave in the refrigerator for a couple of hours.

Peppermint creams

WHAT YOU NEED

* ★ bowl
* ★ mixing spoon
* ★ sieve
* ★ 350g/12oz icing sugar, plus a little extra
* ★ 1 egg white
* ★ peppermint essence
* ★ rolling pin
* ★ pastry cutters
* ★ baking tray
* ★ waxed paper

1. Sieve the icing sugar into a bowl. Add the egg white and a few drops of peppermint essence. Mix to form a very stiff paste.

2. Sprinkle the extra icing sugar on a clean work surface and roll the dough to about 5mm thick.

3. Cut fancy shapes with pastry cutters, and put each shape on waxed paper in a baking tray. You can gather up the scraps, knead them together and roll the sugar paste out again until it is all used up.

4. Leave the peppermint creams out to dry for about a day.

Tips for cooks

Always ask a grown-up if it's OK to do some cooking.

Always wash your hands before you start cooking.

Never use a cooker unless there's a grown-up nearby to help.

Always clear up after cooking. Don't leave the washing-up for someone else to do.

Palm Sunday

The seven days leading up to Easter start with a day of celebration. Palm Sunday is the Sunday before Easter, when Christians remember another special event in Jesus' life.

After three years of travelling the land, healing those who were ill and telling people about God and what it means to believe in him, Jesus became very well known. Thousands of people crowded to hear him speak wherever he went. But some people - especially the religious leaders - did not like what Jesus did. He upset their ideas and they were jealous of his popularity.

At the time Jesus and his twelve friends (the disciples) joined the crowds going to Jerusalem for the great Passover Festival, his enemies were plotting to kill him.

Before entering Jerusalem, Jesus asked his disciples to fetch a donkey for him to ride into the city. It was a young colt, and had never been ridden before, but it let Jesus sit on its back. The people who saw Jesus began cheering. Perhaps this was the time when he would declare himself to be God's chosen king. Some must have hoped that he would lead an army against the Romans, who ruled the country. But he was riding a donkey—a sign that he came in peace.

Everyone shouted for joy. They welcomed him as a king. Some of the crowd threw their cloaks down in the road to carpet his way. Others broke off branches from Palm trees and waved them like flags. The most important week in history had begun.

Palm trees

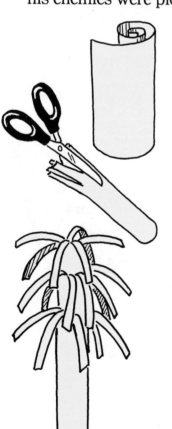

All around the world churches hold special Palm Sunday services. The churches are often decorated with palm leaves, and in some churches palm crosses are handed out. In northern countries, where palm trees will not grow, branches of evergreen yew or budding twigs of hazel or willow are used instead of palm leaves.

Why not make your own little palm tree to wave on Palm Sunday?

WHAT YOU NEED
★ paper, at least 15cm by 30cm
★ scissors
★ glue

1. Roll the paper from the narrow edge to make a tube. Glue to fasten the roll.

2. Make cuts downwards from one end, about a third of the length of the tube.

3. Gently pull out the paper from the centre of the tube, holding the top edge of the cut pieces. Then flatten the cut pieces to create palm leaves.

Plaited donkey

1. Cut nine lengths of string, about 60cm long.

2. Gather the string into groups of three and knot one end. Plait the string. Tie a knot at the end of two of the plaits. For the third, tie a knot a few centimetres before the end. Unravel the remainder and divide the threads in two bunches. Plait each of these, and tie a knot at the end.

3. Fold back these small plaits to make ears. Loop the main plait back on itself to make the head. Bind with string.

4. Gather the three plaits together. Arrange them so the head is on the top and the other pieces form legs. Bind more string around the middle to make the body.

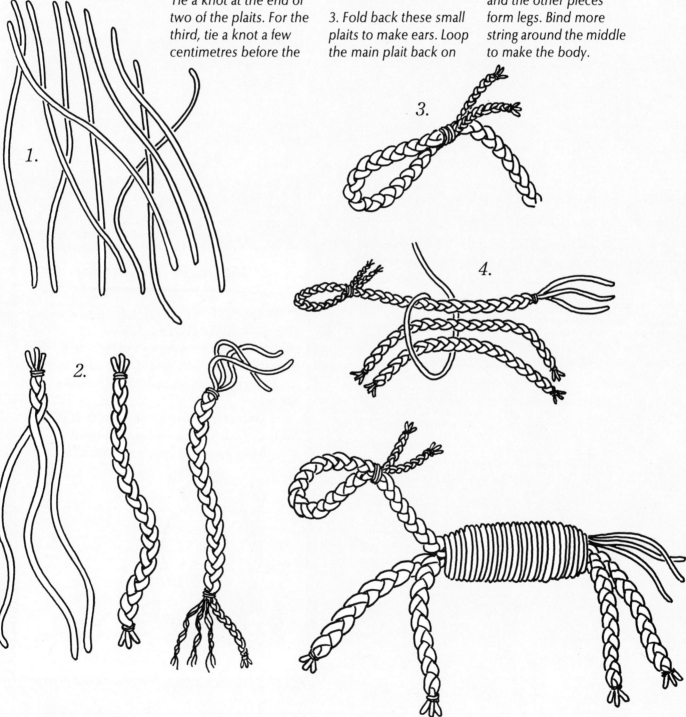

Dark Times

Jesus' triumphant entry into Jerusalem on Palm Sunday proved that many people believed that he was God's own son, the one who would save them. But trouble was brewing for Jesus. The religious leaders were plotting to get rid of him. But they needed someone to help them arrest him when he was away from the crowds. Judas Iscariot, one of Jesus' disciples, was that man.

On Tuesday evening Jesus celebrated the special Passover meal with his disciples. It should have been a happy time, but as they sat down to eat together they all felt sad. Jesus told them he knew that one of them was a traitor. Judas got up and left the room. When he had gone, Jesus took a loaf of bread; he blessed it and gave it to his disciples, telling them that his body would soon be broken like the loaf. Then he took a cup of wine, blessed it and passed it to his disciples, saying that his blood would soon be poured out like the wine, for their sakes.

Jesus told them many things that night that they did not understand until later. He tried to explain that he would soon die, and then be raised to life again - but they could not accept what he said. Peter, one of the disciples, exclaimed that he would rather die than let this happen to Jesus. But Jesus told him that before morning Peter would deny that he had ever known Jesus.

Later that night, Jesus went to a favourite place, the Garden of Gethsemane. He knew that he had been betrayed, and he knew that he would be put to death. Jesus prayed to God, crying out for help to face the awful events which lay ahead.

Suddenly there was noise. Soldiers with clubs and swords appeared through the dark trees. Judas stepped forward and kissed Jesus as a sign to the soldiers that this was the man they wanted. Immediately Peter grabbed a sword and cut off a soldier's ear. But Jesus did not want any violence, so he told Peter to put his sword away and healed the man's ear. Then Jesus was led away, to be tried by the Jewish Court. Although the witnesses disagreed, he was found guilty of a crime against God.

Maundy Thursday

At the special Passover meal, Jesus said he was giving his disciples a new rule or commandment, to love one another. He washed their feet, as servants would have done in those days, to give them an example of humble service.

The Thursday before Easter Sunday is called Maundy Thursday, from the latin word *mandatum* meaning "commandment".

On Friday morning Jesus was taken to the Roman governor, Pilate, for him to agree to the death sentence. But Pilate did not find Jesus guilty by Roman law and offered to release him.

However, the religious leaders had quickly gathered a crowd of supporters to surround Pilate's residence. As soon as the governor announced that he was going to free Jesus, the crowd began to shout, "Crucify! Crucify!". Pilate tried again, saying that since it was the Passover he would set a prisoner free. The crowd shouted for Barabbas, a murderer. Jesus must die. Pilate, afraid of a riot, gave in.

So Jesus was crucified. Hanging from the cross, in great pain, Jesus still asked God to forgive the men who had put him there. At the moment Jesus died, an earthquake shook the country - and one of the tough Roman soldiers who watched him die declared that Jesus must surely be the son of God.

Two friends of Jesus arranged that he should be buried in a cave-like tomb, and a large stone was rolled across the entrance.

Good Friday

Good Friday is the day when Christians remember the Friday that Jesus was crucified.

In Germany it is called Silent Friday and in Greece, Holy or Great Friday.

But why call it good when it is the day we remember Jesus' death? If this were the end of the story there would be nothing good about Good Friday. But, as you will go on to read, the story is far from over...

Bread without yeast

Bread is usually made with yeast. The yeast gives off little bubbles of air as it grows, and this forms bubbles in the dough, making it light and spongy. But it takes a long time to make. Bread without yeast is flat and hard by comparison.

WHAT YOU NEED

★ bowl
★ baking tray
★ oil
★ 250g/8oz plain flour
★ salt
★ milk
★ mixing spoon

1. Ask a grown-up to heat the oven to 180°C.

2. Mix the flour and salt. Add enough milk to make a stiff dough.

3. Oil the baking tray.

4. Shape the dough into rolls and place on the baking tray.

5. Bake for about 15 minutes. This bread must be eaten very fresh, or it becomes even harder!

Jesus is Alive!

EASTER SUNDAY

The next day, Saturday, was the Jewish Sabbath, when no one was allowed to work or make journeys. So it was very early on Sunday morning when some women who were friends of Jesus went to visit the tomb. They were taking sweet-smelling ointment to put on the body, as was the custom. The problem was, how would they roll the great stone back to get inside?

When they reached the tomb, they were amazed to find it was already open. Peering inside, they saw a bright angel, who told them that Jesus was alive. They were terrified by what they had seen. One of them, Mary Magdalene, stood around wondering where the body could be. She saw a man and thought he must be the gardener. Perhaps he would know what had happened. She went and asked him. He answered with just one word: "Mary".

She recognized the voice at once. It was Jesus. He was alive.

Jesus is alive! The friends of Jesus praised God. The word they used was "Hallelujah"—Praise God.

So the sadness of Good Friday is quickly turned to joy. Jesus died and rose to life to bring forgiveness and new life to everyone who will accept his gift: that is something worth celebrating.

Easter garden

WHAT YOU NEED
- ★ shallow dish or tray
- ★ stones
- ★ moss, or green fabric such as felt
- ★ egg-cup or small vase
- ★ flowers

1. Arrange the stones in the tray, to form a mound with a tiny cave at the bottom and a space for the vase at the top.

2. Arrange the moss or fabric over the stones to look like grass.

3. Select a large, round stone to be the door of the cave. Arrange it so that it is rolled back from the opening.

4. Pour a little water into the vase, and arrange some flowers in it. (If you cannot get fresh flowers, make paper flowers like the one described in the instructions for the Mother's Day posy.) Place the vase in the space you have left on top of the mound.

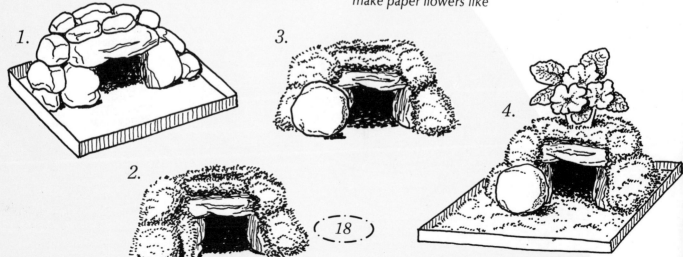

Easter card

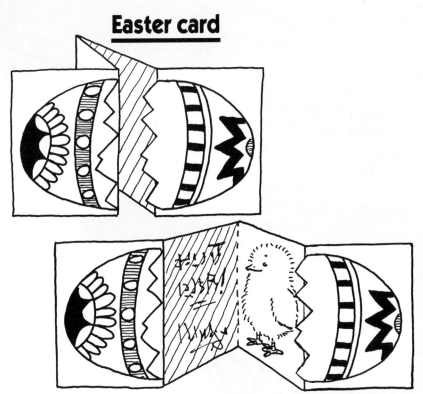

WHAT YOU NEED

★ thin card, 10cm by 29cm

★ crayons

★ ruler

1. Fold the card as shown. Draw the two halves of an egg on the front flaps. Colour them brightly.

2. Open the card and draw in the chick and the greeting. Colour the chick.

Easter nests

WHAT YOU NEED

★ 100g/4oz chocolate

★ 225g/8oz puffed breakfast cereal

★ paper cake cases

★ saucepan

★ teaspoon

★ heatproof basin, to fit inside saucepan

★ mixing spoon

★ small chocolate or sugar eggs

1. Put some water in the saucepan, so that it is about a quarter full. Put the basin in to check that the water does not overflow. If it does, tip a little away.

Ask a grown-up to heat the water to boiling and put it in a safe place for you to use.

2. Put the basin in the water and break the chocolate into the basin. Make sure that no water splashes into the chocolate. Let the chocolate melt and then add the cereal. Stir well. (If you have a microwave, you can melt the chocolate very easily. Put the chocolate in a large bowl made of plastic or china, and heat for 10 seconds at a time on medium power until your chocolate is melted.)

3. Place two or three teaspoonfuls of the mixture into each of the paper cases and press down the centre with the back of the spoon to make a nest shape. Leave to set in a cool place.

4. Fill the nests with small eggs.

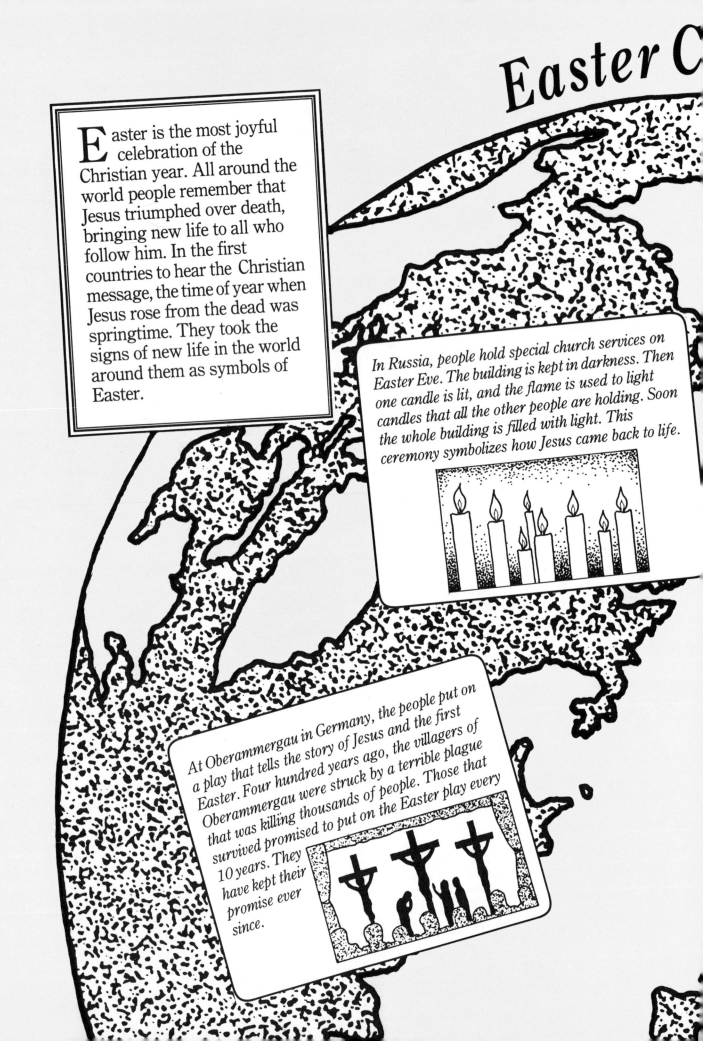

E aster is the most joyful celebration of the Christian year. All around the world people remember that Jesus triumphed over death, bringing new life to all who follow him. In the first countries to hear the Christian message, the time of year when Jesus rose from the dead was springtime. They took the signs of new life in the world around them as symbols of Easter.

In Russia, people hold special church services on Easter Eve. The building is kept in darkness. Then one candle is lit, and the flame is used to light candles that all the other people are holding. Soon the whole building is filled with light. This ceremony symbolizes how Jesus came back to life.

At Oberammergau in Germany, the people put on a play that tells the story of Jesus and the first Easter. Four hundred years ago, the villagers of Oberammergau were struck by a terrible plague that was killing thousands of people. Those that survived promised to put on the Easter play every 10 years. They have kept their promise ever since.

In North America, many people go to a sunrise service at church. The service starts in the dark, before dawn. When the sun rises, it lights up the stained-glass windows and reminds people that Jesus, the light of the world, has risen. Sometimes people from different churches meet together by a lake at dawn.

In Poland, Easter day food is set out ready all day long, so that everyone can eat just when they feel like it. The table is decorated with green leaves and a sugar lamb may be placed as a centre-piece.

In many European languages the name for Easter comes from the word "Passover", which is the name of an important Jewish festival.

Denmark: Paaske

France: Pâcques

Holland: Pasen

Italy: Pasqua

Spain: Pascua

Sweden: Påsk

Wales: Pasg

An Easter Party

Down the ages, people have enjoyed lots of different games and sports at Easter. You can use some of these old traditions in an Easter party.

Easter egg hunt

People have given eggs as gifts from before the time of Christ. They celebrate new life in nature and symbolize the new life that Jesus brings.

You can hide small, foil-wrapped chocolate eggs in all kinds of places around your home. Outside, think of all the places a chicken might hide to lay her eggs.

Egg rolling

Rolling eggs down slopes is popular in many countries. In the United States there is an egg rolling competition on the lawns of the White House, the home of the President, each Easter.

Use hard-boiled eggs. Everyone lines up, as if for a race, and rolls their egg as far as they can. The person whose egg goes the furthest is the winner.

Egg shackling

Find out who has the strongest egg! Players try to crack each other's egg by banging them together. Use hard-boiled eggs!

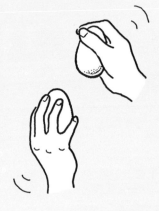

Egg throwing

Each player has an egg. The idea is to throw it into the air and catch it. The first person to drop their egg on the ground is the loser.

Use the hard-boiled eggs to make egg filling for sandwiches. Simply chop up the eggs with salt and a little milk, yoghurt or mayonnaise. Use the mixture to make sandwiches.

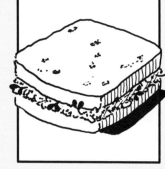

Why not grow seeds to make your sandwiches more interesting?

Alfafa seeds

1. Make holes in the lid of a clean jam jar.

2. Fill the jar with water and add the alfafa seeds.

3. Put the lid back on and turn the jar upside-down so that the water drains away.

4. Repeat twice a day for three days and the seeds should sprout.

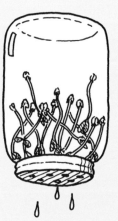

Cress seeds

1. Lay a piece of damp blotting paper or tissue on a shallow tray. Sprinkle cress seed on to it.

2. Make sure the blotting paper stays damp, but not too wet.

3. Cress seeds take about 10 days to grow.

Easter bonnets

People used to wear new clothes at Easter, including a fancy hat. Make Easter bonnets to wear at the party.

Daffodil bonnet

1. Cut a piece of thick paper to the shape shown.

2. Glue the edges together to form a bonnet shape.

3. Cut a strip of paper to the length of the front edge of your bonnet and carefully glue it in position.

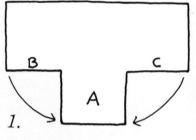

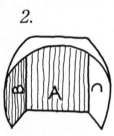

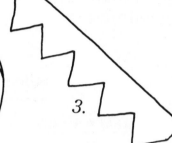

Flower bonnet

1. Cut a circle from a piece of thick card. (Draw around a large dinner plate to get an even circle.) Cut a slit in the circle from the outer edge to the middle and make into a cone shape as shown.

2. Make some flowers out of tissue paper to decorate your hat.

3. Attach a strip of crepe paper to either side so that you can fasten your bonnet.

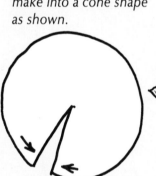

Bunny bonnet

1. Measure around your head and then cut a strip of thick paper a few centimetres longer than the measurement.

2. Cut some ear shapes from the card and attach them to the head-band.

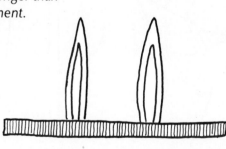

Whitsun

For forty days after he rose from the dead, Jesus appeared many times to his friends. He proved to them quite clearly that he was alive again. But after that time he was taken up to heaven. Even though Jesus had returned to his Father in heaven, he did not leave his followers feeling lost and alone. God's Holy Spirit was sent to comfort and strengthen them. The same Spirit can fill people with new life, love and strength today.

Windmill

Wind is often used as a symbol of God and his power. We can see the effect of wind, but not the wind itself.

WHAT YOU NEED

★ stiff paper, 20cm square

★ crayons

★ scissors

★ drawing pin

★ button

★ thin dowel, about 40cm long

1. Draw a pattern on both sides of the paper.

2. Make four cuts from the corners towards the centre.

3. Fold the corners to the centre point as shown. Push a pin through all thicknesses.

4. Put the pin through one of the holes in a button and then pin the windmill on to the stick.

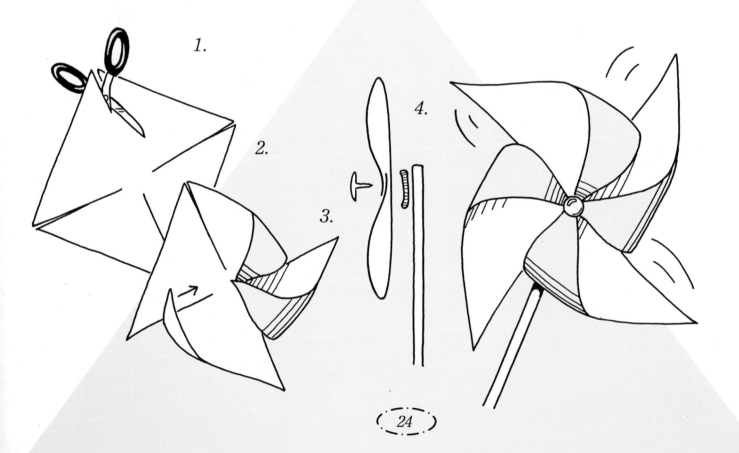

Writing paper

Whitsun marks the time when the followers of Jesus began sharing the good news about him. When you have good news, you want to tell other people about it too. Why not write a letter to friends who live too far away for you to visit, using writing paper that you have decorated yourself?

WHAT YOU NEED

★ plain writing paper and envelopes
★ black marker
★ ruler
★ red and yellow paint
★ stiff paintbrush
★ old toothbrush
★ adhesive putty

1. Use a black marker to rule a border on a sheet of writing paper.

2. Trace the border on to a second sheet. Cut out the small rectangle from the second sheet.

3. Lay another sheet over the paper with the border. Fasten the small rectangle in the right position, using tiny blobs of adhesive putty.

4. Dip your paintbrush in yellow paint. Flick the bristles with your toothbrush, so the paint splatters on to your paper. Repeat all round the border.

Do the same with the red paint, to create a bright speckled pattern.

5. Remove the centre rectangle.

6. Use the same technique to decorate more sheets of paper, and your envelopes. You can try cutting borders of different shapes.

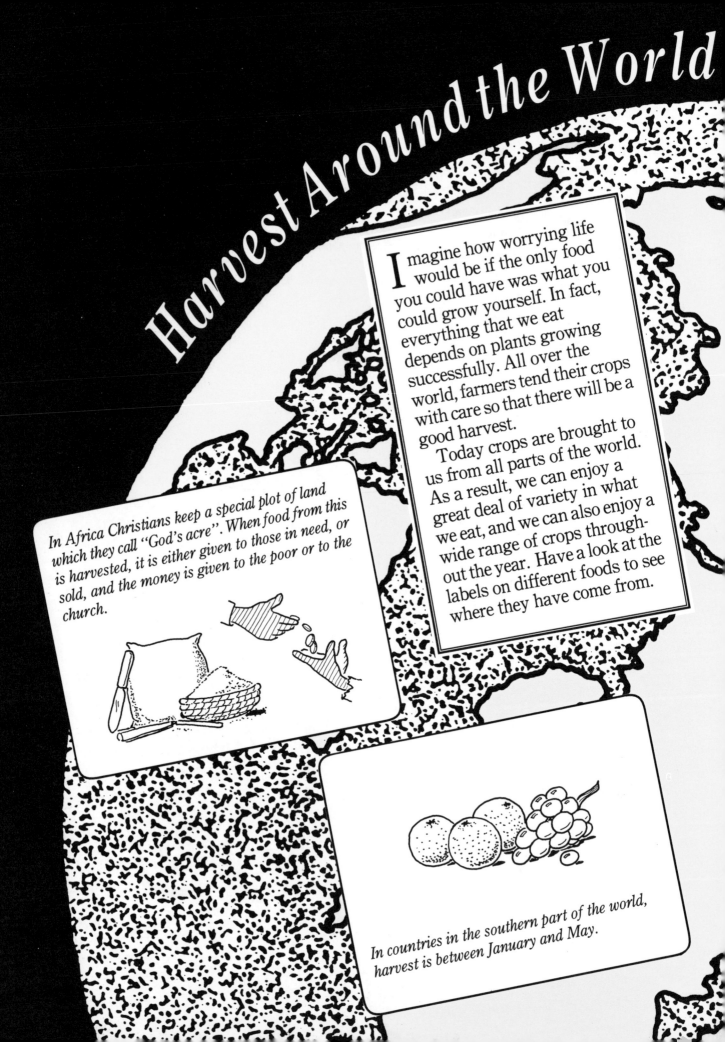

Imagine how worrying life would be if the only food you could have was what you could grow yourself. In fact, everything that we eat depends on plants growing successfully. All over the world, farmers tend their crops with care so that there will be a good harvest.

Today crops are brought to us from all parts of the world. As a result, we can enjoy a great deal of variety in what we eat, and we can also enjoy a wide range of crops throughout the year. Have a look at the labels on different foods to see where they have come from.

In Africa Christians keep a special plot of land which they call "God's acre". When food from this is harvested, it is either given to those in need, or sold, and the money is given to the poor or to the church.

In countries in the southern part of the world, harvest is between January and May.

In the countries in the northern part of the world, the main harvest is between July and October.

In South India the harvest festival is called Pongol. Animals are decorated and fed with good food. The people dance and sing, eat special food and thank God for his goodness.

Tropical countries may have more than one harvest time each year.

Thanking God

At harvest time, Christians often celebrate by decorating churches with flowers, fruit and vegetables and going to services of thanksgiving. They want to say thank you to God, who has made a world that provides us with everything we need.

The psalms are the hymnbook of the Jewish people. They were written thousands of years ago and can be found in the Old Testament of the Bible. This psalm praises God for the way he provides a harvest. God is still the same today.

You show your care for the land
*   by sending rain;*
*   you make it rich and fertile.*

You fill the streams with water;
*   you provide the earth with crops.*

This is how you do it:
*   you send abundant rain*
*   on the ploughed fields*
*   and soak them with water;*
*   you soften the soil with showers*
*   and cause the young plants to grow.*

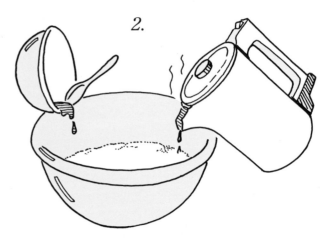

What a rich harvest your goodness provides!

You can read more about how God cares for his people in Psalm 65 in the Bible.

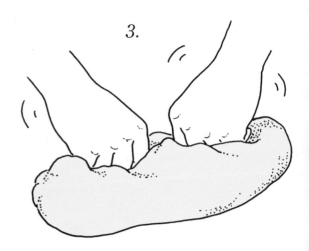

Harvest loaf

WHAT YOU NEED

★ 500g/18oz strong white flour

★ salt

★ 12g/½ oz dried yeast

★ 1 teaspoon sugar

★ 1 egg yolk

★ pastry brush

★ 300ml/ ½ pint warm water

★ large mixing bowl

★ mixing spoon

★ plastic wrap

★ baking tray

★ oil

★ kitchen scissors

1. Dissolve the sugar in about 100ml/4floz of the warm water and stir in the dried yeast. Put in a warm place until it bubbles.

2. Mix the flour and salt together in a bowl. Add the yeast mixture, and enough extra warm water to make a stiff ball of dough.

3. Knead the dough by flattening it with the heel of your hand and folding it over. Knead it until the dough springs back to shape when you press it.

4. Place the dough in the bowl, cover with plastic wrap, and leave in a warm place until it is twice its original size.

Oil a baking tray.

Ask a grown-up to heat the oven to 200°C.

Knead the dough for two more minutes, and then divide it into about twenty pieces.

5. Roll each piece into a long thin shape, slightly fatter at one end. Brush the fatter end with egg yolk. Snip the fat end to make little peaks that look like seed kernels on an ear of corn.

Arrange the pieces on the baking tray to look like a sheaf of corn. Arrange the last piece so that it looks as if it ties the pieces together.

Cover lightly with plastic wrap and leave to rise for about 30 minutes.

Bake the loaf for about 35 minutes. Ask a grown-up to help you lift it out of the oven, and leave to cool.

4.

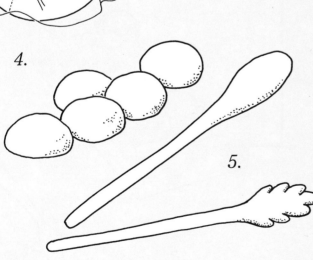

5.

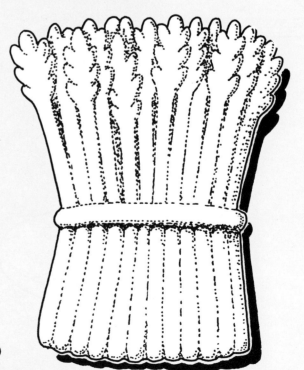

Harvest Treats

1.

2.

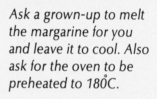

Carrot muffins

WHAT YOU NEED

★ 175g/6oz self-raising flour

★ 75g/3oz brown sugar

★ 50g/2oz coconut

★ 1/2 teaspoon salt

★ 1 teaspoon allspice

★ 50g/2oz margarine

★ 2 eggs

★ 50ml/2fl oz milk

★ 2 medium-sized carrots, weighing about 150g/5oz in total

★ saucepan

★ two mixing bowls

★ tablespoon

★ whisk

★ grater

★ paper cake cases

★ baking tin

★ cardboard box

★ plastic wrap

Ask a grown-up to melt the margarine for you and leave it to cool. Also ask for the oven to be preheated to 180°C.

1. Mix together the flour, sugar, coconut, salt and allspice in one bowl.

2. In the other bowl, whisk together the margarine, eggs and milk.

3. Grate the carrots finely. Add the grated carrot to the milk mixture.

4. Now pour the liquid mixture into the dry mixture and stir just enough to mix.

5. Arrange the cake cases on the baking tin and put a spoonful of mixture in each. This quantity makes about 12 muffins.

Bake the muffins for 12–15 minutes. Ask a grown-up to help you lift the hot baking tin out of the oven.

Fill a gift box with your muffins. Find a plain cardboard box that will hold them neatly. Cover it with harvest gift wrap, made using fruit and vegetable prints. Cover the top with plastic wrap.

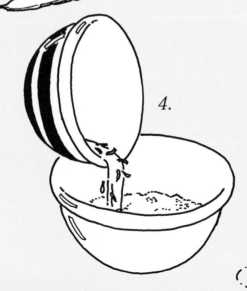

3.

4.

5.

Fruit and vegetable prints

Fruits and vegetables have interesting patterns in them. Cut an apple in half and look carefully at the core in the centre. You should be able to see the brown pips, or seeds. Cut a Brussels sprout in half and observe the layers of leaves. Notice the rings inside the top of a carrot. Try printing with these fruits and vegetables.

WHAT YOU NEED

★ fruits and vegetables, cut in half

★ poster paint and brushes

★ white paper

1. Brush paint over the cut half of your fruit or vegetable.

2. Press it carefully on to the paper to leave a print.

Build up a print pattern in this way.

Marzipan fruits

WHAT YOU NEED

★ ready-made marzipan

★ red, green and orange food colouring

★ three small bowls

★ whole cloves

★ cocktail stick

★ paintbrush

★ food grater

★ small paper cases

★ small, shallow box

★ foil

★ plastic wrap

1. Divide the marzipan into four. Use one quarter to make bananas. Break off small pieces and shape them into bananas. Join several together to make a bunch and then put them into a paper case.

2. Put another quarter into a bowl with a few drops of red food colouring. Work it together until the marzipan is red. Break off small pieces and shape them to look like straw-berries. Using a cocktail stick, make marks like seeds on the outside. Put a clove in the top, for the hull of each strawberry, and put each in a paper case.

3. Put the third quarter in a bowl with some green food colouring. Work it together until the marzipan is green. Break off small pieces and work into the shapes of apples. Push a clove in the top of each. Dip a paintbrush into red food colouring and paint on some rosy parts. Put each apple into a paper case.

4. Mix the last quarter of marzipan with some orange vegetable dye. Mix this in well and then shape the marzipan into oranges. Press the oranges against a grater to make the indentations and put each orange into a paper case.

5. Cover the box with foil. Arrange the fruits in the box. Cover the top with plastic wrap.

Remember to remove the cloves before you eat the sweets!

31

Harvest Gifts

Lavender bundle

This pretty gift can be hung in a room or put in a drawer to give a lavender scent.

1.

WHAT YOU NEED

★ nine long flower stems of lavender

★ wool, about 4m long

1. Tie the heads of the flower stems together tightly with wool.

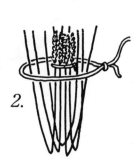
2.

2. Carefully bend the stems upwards to cover the heads. Tie the stems at the bottom of the flower part.

3. Weave the wool under and over the stems in turn, continuing right to

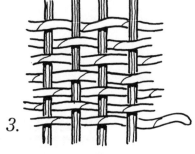
3.

the bottom. Secure with a knot.

4. Trim the stalks to make them even.

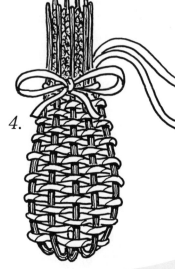
4.

Straw pictures

The long, shiny stalks of wheat and oats are harvested as straw. The straw has a very practical use, as bedding for animals, but in many parts of the world people use it in all kinds of artistic ways. In Byelorussia, straw pictures are made.

1.

WHAT YOU NEED

★ thick card

★ black paint and paintbrush

★ straw

★ bowl of water

★ glue

★ scissors

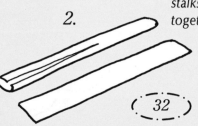
2.

1. Cut a rectangle the size you want your finished picture to be. Paint it black. Leave to dry.

2. Soak straw stalks in water, and slit each one with your thumbnail so you can open it out and flatten it.

3. Try cutting straw into different lengths, and see what kinds of patterns and shapes you can make. Use a combination of single stalks and stalks placed close together to make blocks.

4. When you are happy with your picture, glue the straw in place.

Stick a border around your card, to finish the picture.

Pumpkin friends

For this project, you need to use fruits that have been stored in an airy place to dry out.

WHAT YOU NEED

★ smooth-skinned gourds, pumpkins, marrows or squash

★ black wax crayon

★ old pen or ball-point, or a nail

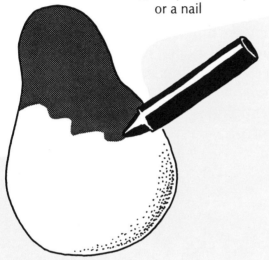

1. Begin by washing your fruit or pumpkin. Leave it until the skin is quite dry.

2. Rub all over the skin with a black wax crayon, until the surface is thickly covered. Polish the wax coating with your hand to make it shiny.

3. Look at the shape of your fruit or pumpkin. Who does its shape remind you of? When you have decided, scrape the design with a pen or nail, to leave the natural colour of the gourd showing through.

Take care not to leave your fruit or pumpkin friend anywhere where it might get too hot, such as a sunny windowsill, as the wax may soften and leave a mark.

Seed necklaces

Seeds come in a great range of shapes, colours and sizes. This project uses fairly large seeds. See how many different types you can find. Melon seeds, sunflower seeds and bean seeds are all good choices.

WHAT YOU NEED

★ a selection of different seeds

★ strong needle

★ thin cord or strong sewing thread

★ scissors

1. Try different arrangements of seeds to give the effect you want. Thread them together carefully, piercing the centre of each with your needle.

2. Make a long string of seeds. When this string makes a loop long enough to go over your head, knot the ends together carefully.

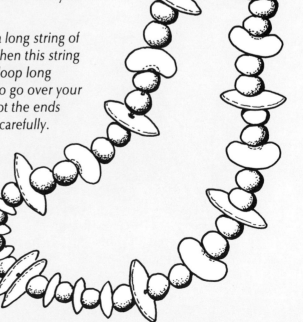

Thanksgiving

In the United States of America, the fourth Thursday in November is called Thanksgiving Day. It is an important family and religious festival which remembers the first service of thanksgiving for the harvest of 1621, celebrated by the Pilgrim Fathers. They were a group of Dutch and English emigrants who sailed from Plymouth, on the south coast of England, in September 1620. Their ship was called the *Mayflower*. They landed in America three months later.

The settlers first farmed the land in 1621 with the help of the native Indians, and they celebrated their first harvest thanksgiving with them.

Americans celebrate Thanksgiving by decorating their houses with autumn flowers and fruit and attending church services and Thanksgiving dinners. Traditional foods at these meals include roast turkey with cranberry sauce, pumpkin pie, sweet potatoes and sweet-corn.

The first European settlers in North America were astonished at the wild turkeys they found there: large ugly birds which made a funny gobbling noise. But turkey meat is delicious, and one turkey is enough for a large party!

Indian corn, or maize, grows about 2m tall. Its seeds are arranged in large seed heads, called cobs. On the plant they are covered with a sheath of green leaves. You cook cobs by taking off the sheath and boiling the cobs for a few minutes. Then eat the cobs with salt and butter. Messy!

Pumpkin pie

Everyone loves a big round pumpkin, but what do you do with them? Pumpkin pie is made by scooping out the flesh inside and boiling it till it is soft and pulpy. This is mixed with eggs, cream and spices. You either love it or you hate it!

WHAT YOU NEED

★ pastry case (ask a grown-up to make one for you).

★ 2 eggs

★ 175g/6oz cooked, sieved pumpkin (or tinned pumpkin)

★ 75g/3oz sugar

★ ½ teaspoon salt

★ 1 teaspoon cinnamon

★ ½ teaspoon ginger

★ ¼ teaspoon ground cloves

★ 300ml/½ pint condensed milk or single cream

★ mixing bowl

★ whisk

★ teaspoon

★ wooden spoon

★ whipped cream or vanilla ice cream

Ask a grown-up to pre-heat the oven to 210°C.

1. Crack the eggs into the bowl and whisk.

2. Mix in the pumpkin, and then add the sugar, salt, cinnamon, ginger and ground cloves.

3. Add the milk or cream and mix everything together.

4. Pour the mixture into the pastry shell.

Bake the pie for 15 minutes at 210°C. Then ask a grown-up to turn the oven down to 180°C and bake the pie for another 45 minutes.

Allow it to cool and serve with the cream or ice cream.

1.

2.

3.

4.

All Saints' and All Souls'

November 1st is All Saints' Day, when Christians remember those Christians of days gone by whose lives were a shining example of how to live as Jesus taught. The following day is All Souls' Day, when Christians remember all people who have died.

Christians believe they have good news to share with everyone. When Jesus died and returned to life again he broke the power of death, and proved that his promise of eternal life was true. Although people miss friends and relatives who have died, Christians can be glad that death is not the end, but the gateway to a new and better life with Jesus.

Saint picture

Stained-glass windows decorate many old churches. Sometimes you will find a picture of a saint, and a scene from one of the stories that are told about them.

Stained glass looks beautiful during the day, but at night you can hardly see it from inside the building. It is only beautiful when the sun is shining through it.

In a similar way, the saints are not important because of who they were and what they did: they are important because people could see God "shining" through them.

WHAT YOU NEED

★ tracing paper
★ marker pens, including black
★ adhesive putty

1. Notice how a stained-glass picture is made up of coloured bits of glass set into black lead frames. Draw a picture on the tracing paper using a black marker for the black frames. Then colour your picture using bright colours.

Use adhesive putty to fasten your picture to a window. The light will shine through it.

Here's an idea for your own stained-glass window. Saint Francis of Assisi was a wealthy young man. He gave up all his money to become a preacher, telling people about God. He had a great love for all God's creatures. Pictures of St Francis often show him preaching to the birds.

Family tree mobile

Find out about the people in your family. To make the mobile, you will have to choose either your father's family or your mother's family. (You can make another mobile later.) Ask your parents and grandparents for the information you need. You may also have a family photo album that will help you.

Find out the names of your grandparents. Write down their names.

Find out the names of all their children. Write these down on a line below.

Find out whom they married, and write these names next to theirs. Write down the names of all their children on a line below. Don't forget to include yourself!

If you don't already know, try to find out what each of these people look like.

WHAT YOU NEED

★ thin card
★ pencils and crayons
★ scissors
★ strong sewing cotton
★ needle
★ adhesive putty

1. Draw each of the people on your family tree on thin card. Draw the front, then cut out the figure and draw the back.

Arrange all the figures on a table, with each generation on a row of its own. Cut pieces of card long enough to hold each row in a line.

2. Thread your needle, and knot one end. Sew each figure, one at a time, to the strip of card above, and knot it.

3. Use adhesive putty to hang your mobile.

If your mobile seems to be too heavy at one end, try sticking a piece of adhesive putty to the lighter end to balance it.

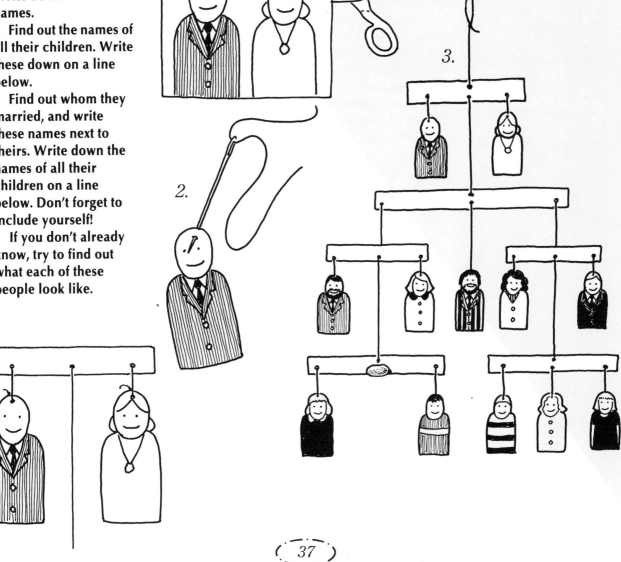

37

Afraid of the Dark?

All Saints' Day is sometimes called All Hallows', because "hallow" is an old word for saint. The eve of All Hallows' is called Hallowe'en, and some people have Hallowe'en parties. Many of the customs go back to the days before Christianity, when people were very afraid of darkness—and of the evil spirits and witches they thought roamed around in the dark. They would dress up in ugly disguises, so that the evil spirits would not recognize them but would be frightened away. But Christians know that they have nothing to fear because Jesus has defeated the powers of evil. He is "the light of the world".

Darkness itself is not something to be feared. God made night as well as day, and all kinds of interesting creatures that are out and about at night. The more we find out about them, the less scary they seem.

Dear God

Even darkness is not dark for you

and the night is as bright as the day.

Keep me safe in the dark even when I feel afraid.

Owl picture

There are several types of owl, but all have large eyes to help them see at night. They hear well and fly silently in order to catch their prey of small mammals, snails, small birds and frogs. They swallow their prey whole. The bits that they can't digest, such as the bones and feathers, are brought up as pellets.

Collect a variety of seed pods, grasses and leaves to make this picture.

WHAT YOU NEED

★ seed pods, grasses and leaves
★ paper
★ glue
★ dark paint

1. Mix your paint till it is very thin, and use a very wet brush to give a thin wash of colour all over your paper. Let it dry.

2. Create a picture of an owl using the different materials that you have found. Try to give the texture of smooth, soft front feathers and of strong soft flying feathers on the wings. The owl also needs a fierce hooked beak and large round eyes.

Bat mobile

Bats are the only mammals that can truly fly. Their wings are made of thin skin supported by long finger bones. Some bats feed on fruit. Others hunt insects in the air. In order to find insects in the darkness, bats make a series of high-pitched squeaks. If the sound hits an insect, an echo bounces back to the bat telling it the position of its food. This is called echolocation.

WHAT YOU NEED

★ paper plate
★ thin string
★ black card
★ small pieces of kitchen foil
★ small pieces of plastic wrap
★ dark cotton
★ needle
★ scissors
★ sticky tape

1. Cut bat shapes as shown, and fold the wings. Thread the needle, and attach each bat to a long piece of cotton.

2. To make insects, cut the foil into long, thin triangles and roll up into a cylinder, beginning at the wide end. Cut a tiny square of plastic wrap and pinch together in the centre. Attach the plastic wing to the metal body by winding cotton thread around in a figure-of-eight, and knot. Leave a long piece of thread hanging from each.

3. Now attach the cotton from each creature to the rim of the paper plate using sticky tape. Attach a thread to the centre of the plate, and suspend your mobile.

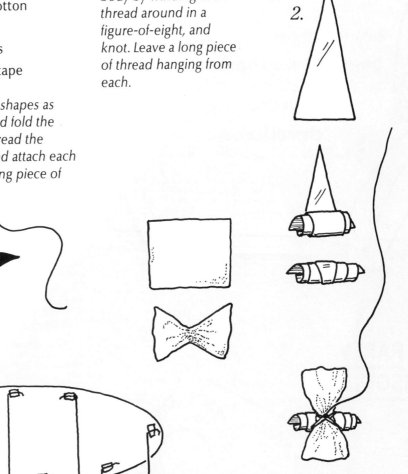

This mobile looks very realistic in a darkened room, when the insects catch any gleams of light, and the bats look like dark shadows.

A Nocturnal Party

Menu

Baked potatoes in their jackets
bowls of baked beans or chilli

harvest apples
chocolate cake

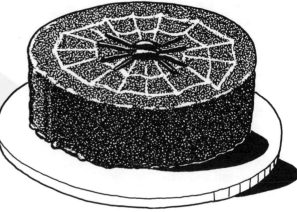

Decorate your cake with a spider's web.
First cover the cake with chocolate icing,
made with about 225g/8oz icing sugar
with a tablespoonful of cocoa plus enough
water to make a very thick, stiff paste.
Then make white icing from icing sugar and
a little water and dribble it in a spiral
around the cake, starting at the middle.
Quickly draw lines from the centre out-
wards with a cocktail stick.

Make a spider from chocolate buttons and
chocolate sticks to put in the centre!

PARTY DISGUISES

Paper bag owl head. Be sure to use paper, not plastic!

Bat glasses

Party Games

What's that noise?

When you are out at night, you can't rely only on what you see to know what's going on. Sit your friends in a dark room, and see if they can guess how you are making these noises!

★ Half fill a glass with water, and run your finger around the rim. The vibrations will make a wailing sound.

★ Whistle into a bottle with a narrow neck to make an eerie echo.

★ Hold a thick blade of grass between your thumbs. Blow through it for a wild squealing noise.

★ Tie a piece of elastic to the back of a chair and pull it quite tight. Pluck it, and at the same time let it slacken off.

★ Put rice in a plastic bottle. Roll it slowly.

Shadow play

Put on a shadow play about night-time in the forest. Cut-out trees make good scenery. You could fix these in place on a strip of card.

A hunting scene is exciting (try fox and rabbits).

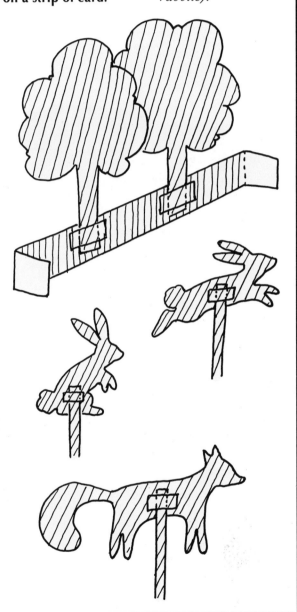

Christmas is Here!

Everyone has a birthday. No one knows the exact date when Jesus was born. We only know that he was born in the land we now call Israel at the time of King Herod the Great, when the Roman Emperor Augustus ruled over the land.

The followers of Jesus wanted to remember his birthday. But when? In the countries where the first Christians lived many other people celebrated mid-winter festivals. The days were short, and nights long and dark, and they needed something to cheer them up and remind them that springtime would soon be on the way. What better time could there be to remember Jesus, who brings light to the world whatever the time of year, with the promise of a new and joyful way of living?

The Christmas Story

Long ago, in a small house in a village called Nazareth, in the country we call Israel, lived a young woman called Mary. She was engaged to Joseph, the village carpenter. One day when she was busy in the house, an angel came to her, with a special message from God.

"Mary, God is going to send his son into the world as he promised. He has chosen you to be the mother of his son. You are to call the baby Jesus." Mary was astonished but she felt very glad that God had chosen her for this honour. The angel then visited Joseph to tell him the message too.

Several months later, when the baby was almost due to be born, everyone in the country was ordered by the Roman emperor to return to their home town to be counted. Joseph's family came from a small town called Bethlehem, so he set out with his wife on the long journey. Of course, many people were travelling for the same reason, so there wasn't much room for all the visitors to stay. At last, Mary and Joseph were offered shelter in a room normally used by the animals. There Mary had her baby. She called him Jesus and used a manger—an animal's feedbox—as his first cradle.

Out on the hillsides, shepherds were watching over their sheep when suddenly a bright light filled the sky. An angel spoke to them saying:

"Do not be afraid. I bring you great news. God's son has been born in Bethlehem. Go and worship him."

The angel was then joined by many others who sang:

"Glory to God in heaven and peace to men on earth."

When the angels had gone, the shepherds made sure their sheep were safe and went straight away to Bethlehem. There in the room for the animals they found Mary, Joseph and the special baby. They knelt and worshipped Jesus.

In the East there lived wise men who studied the stars. One night they saw a bright new star. It meant that a new king had been born. They, too, decided to go to worship him. In order to find him, they followed the bright star. Each wise man took a special gift to give to the new king.

The star took them to a capital city, called Jerusalem. They naturally went to King Herod's palace asking to see the new king. Herod was worried and jealous, for he knew of no new king and feared that a rival would come and overthrow him. He sent the wise men away, telling them to let him know when they found the new king so that he could go and worship him. But Herod did not really want to worship this baby, he wanted to kill him.

The star led the wise men to Bethlehem and the room where Mary was with Jesus. They gave him gifts of gold, frankincense and myrrh. God warned the visitors from the East not to return to Herod because he meant to harm Jesus. The wise men went home another way. Joseph took Mary and Jesus to Egypt for a while, where they could live in safety.

Nativity Plays

Nativity plays act out the main events of the Christmas story. You may have a chance to take part in a play at your school or in a church. You might like to get together with some friends to create your own play for your family and friends.

Here are some ideas for costumes.

Costumes for the Christmas story

The best costumes are fun to make and safe and comfortable to wear.

★ Use non-flammable material whenever possible.

★ Cut flowing robes to a few inches above the ankle, particularly if you have to go up or down stairs in them.

★ Stay away from fire, including candles.

All these costumes require only simple sewing equipment and materials:

★ cloth

★ fabric scissors

★ thread to match the cloth

★ needle

★ measuring tape

Use a knot like this at the beginning and end of your sewing, to hold the thread in place. Running stitch is quick and easy. Make each stitch quite small— about 3mm—or the stitching will not be very strong.

A tunic is made from two rectangles sewn together at the shoulders. Add two smaller rectangles for the sleeves and sew all along the sides of the tunic. Make a cut at the neck so you can fit your head through!

This cloak is very easy. You cut two rectangles to fit you and stitch the shoulders together. Cut an opening right down the front.
If your fabric unravels easily, you can turn the edge under about 1.5cm and stitch it in place.

Make a headdress in a light-coloured fabric, plain or with stripes.

You can make a suitable hat, something between a turban and a fez, from simple materials.

> **If you really can't sew, you can staple the fabric together. It can be a bit scratchy, so remember to wear an old T-shirt underneath!**

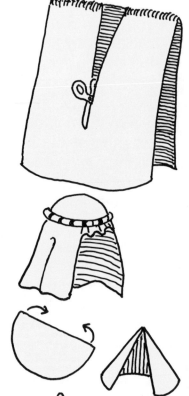

As you act out your nativity play, or simply dress up in your costumes, try to think about what the story really means.

Angels are God's messengers. No one really knows what they look like. The Bible sometimes describes them as wearing white and being very bright to look at. Traditionally, angels are shown with a circle of light, called a halo, around their head. A circle of tinsel on the head gives the right effect.

Mary would have worn a cloak for travelling, perhaps in brown, and a blue dress. Tie the dress at the waist with a strip of fabric. Add a white headdress to complete the costume.

Joseph and the shepherds were all working men. For each of their costumes make a tunic in natural colours such as brown, yellow, white or black, either plain or perhaps with stripes. Tie a length of fabric around the waist as a girdle, or use a leather belt.

For travelling and for working outdoors at night, the men would wear a cloak too. Ideally this should be in a heavier fabric than the tunic, but should also be plain or striped.

Choose expensive-looking fabrics for the tunics and cloaks of the three wise men. Add jewellery if you are able to borrow some.

Today Christians all over the world celebrate the birth of Jesus. For those who live in northern countries, Christmas is still in the middle of winter. People think of sledges for travelling over snow, and candles to light up a dark night. In other parts of the world Christmas is hot and sunny. It is midsummer in the southern countries.

In Canada a long, cold winter is beginning. Some churches decorate their tree with brightly-coloured mittens that people have knitted from leftover wool. After Christmas, the mittens are given to the children, who will need several pairs throughout the months ahead.

In Mexico people light bonfires and let off fireworks just as Christmas Day begins. The many-coloured sparks shine out in the dark night.

In Poland Christmas Eve is known as the Festival of the Star. A feast begins as soon as the first star appears. At the meal, a place is always set for the baby Jesus. After everyone has eaten, there is more celebration as candles on the tree are lit and carols are sung. Presents are brought in by boys dressed as the three wise men.

In South India Christians light little oil lamps and put them on the edge of their low, flat-roofed houses. When people ask them why they have lamps even though it is not dark, they tell them about Jesus, who has brought light to the world.

In Australia Christmas time is hot and sunny. Many people celebrate Christmas on the beach.

Getting Ready for Christmas

When Christmas is only a month away it's time to get busy! There are so many things to get ready in time for Christmas, so much to look forward to.

The four weeks leading up to Christmas are called Advent. The word comes from a Latin word meaning "arrival" or "to come". It is a time in the church year when people look forward to celebrating the arrival of Jesus in this world.

The activities in this section have been specially chosen to help you prepare for Christmas.

Advent calendar

An Advent calendar gives you a surprise door to open for every day in December, ending on Christmas Eve. By the end, you also have a pretty Christmas decoration.

WHAT YOU NEED

★ paper or thin card, 1m by 50cm
★ scissors
★ green and brown paints
★ scraps of Christmas wrapping paper
★ foil, 20cm square
★ red wool, about 1m long
★ 24 pieces of paper, about 3cm by 10cm
★ glue
★ adhesive putty
★ crayons
★ old Christmas cards

1. Draw a Christmas tree on your large piece of paper. Paint it green with a brown tub.

Cut circles from the scraps of wrapping paper to look like baubles. Glue them to the tree.

Cut a star from the foil and glue it to the top of the tree.

Fasten the paper to a door or wall using adhesive putty.

2. Fold each of your small pieces of paper in half. Colour or pattern the outsides and number them from 1 to 24.

3. Inside, either draw a picture of something that makes you think of Christmas, or cut a picture from a Christmas card and glue it on.

Glue each piece over the wool so that it hangs like a flag, but only put a little dab of glue on the inside fold or it will not open.

Put a tiny piece of adhesive putty in the centre of each flag to keep it closed.

4. Glue the thread to the tree, so that it hangs like a chain.

Open a flag each day, beginning on 1 December.

1.

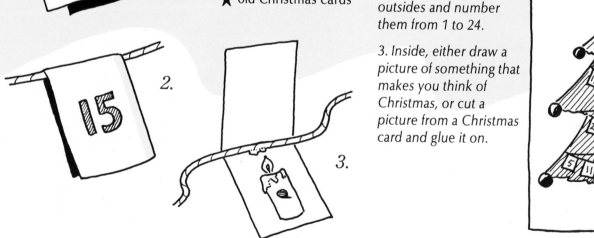

2.

3.

4.

Advent begins on the fourth Sunday before Christmas. The Christian church had a tradition of lighting one special candle on each of those Sundays. By Christmas, four candles were lit. Many people still keep this tradition, in their churches and in their homes.

You can make a special Advent ring of candles and light one candle for a short time each Sunday—perhaps when you and your family have a meal together. It all adds to the excitement of looking forward to Christmas—and celebrating the birth of Jesus, "the light of the world".

Advent ring

1.

2.

WHAT YOU NEED

★ thick card, 20cm square
★ Christmas wrapping paper, 20cm square
★ glue
★ plate, 20cm diameter
★ pencil
★ scissors
★ eight plastic cups or yoghurt pots
★ double-sided tape
★ four pieces flower foam to fit inside cups
★ evergreen sprigs
★ Christmas-tree baubles and ties
★ plaster of Paris
★ glitter
★ four candles

1. Glue the wrapping paper on to the card. When the glue is dry, lay the plate on the card and draw a circle. Cut out the circle shape.

2. Trim the cups or pots so that they are only 3.5cm high. Tape them around the edge of your card circle using double-sided tape.

3. Mix about eight tablespoons of plaster of Paris with enough water to make a thick cream. Pour the mixture into every other pot so that four are about three-quarters full. Push a candle into each of these pots and sprinkle the surface of the plaster with glitter.

4. Soak the flower foam in water. Place it in the other four pots and arrange the evergreens in it. Tie baubles to the evergreens. Ask a grown-up to help you when you light the candles. Never leave candles burning if you go out of the room—blow them out carefully.

Did you know?

In Norway families light a candle every evening from Christmas Eve until New Year.

3.

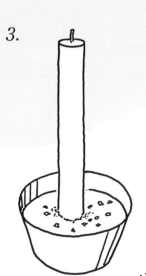

4.

49

Christmas Greetings for All Your Friends

At Christmas time many people send each other cards. It is a good way to stay in touch with friends who live too far away for you to visit. Think about them as you make your card, and don't forget to write a message inside.

Sheep on the hillside card

WHAT YOU NEED

★ thin card, about 20cm by 15cm

★ crayons

★ scissors

★ star sticker

★ cotton balls

★ small piece of black paper

★ glue

1. Fold the card width-ways.

2. Draw a line of hill shapes on the front, and colour the hills green. Cut out the sky area above the line of hills.

3. Open the card. Colour the sky on the right hand side to just below the level of the hills. *Stick a star shape high in the sky.*

4. Shut the card again and glue small pieces of cotton wool to the hillside for sheep. Crayon in black legs. Cut heads from black paper and stick into position.

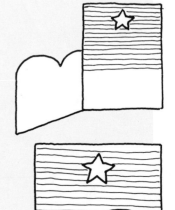

Nativity scene

WHAT YOU NEED

★ thin card, about 20cm by 12cm

★ crayons

1. Fold the 12cm sides in towards the centre, to make "doors". Draw a door across the join.

2. Open the card and draw Mary, Joseph and the baby in the centre part of the card.

Draw the shepherds on the left, and the wise men on the right.

Star letter-card

WHAT YOU NEED

★ stiff paper, about 10cm by 60cm

★ scissors

★ ruler

★ pen, pencil and crayons

★ glue

★ glitter

1. Fold the paper concertina-fashion.

2. Use the ruler to draw a six-pointed star. Take care to leave each "point" about 5mm wide. Spread glue over the front star and sprinkle with glitter.

3. Cut round the star shape. Open up your concertina card and write a letter to a friend, or draw pictures to tell him or her your news.

3.

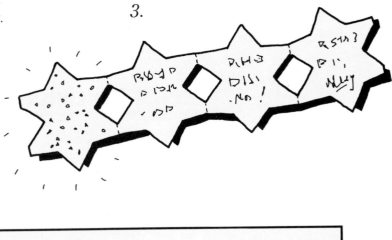

1.

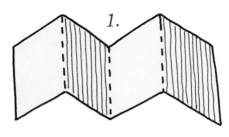

2.

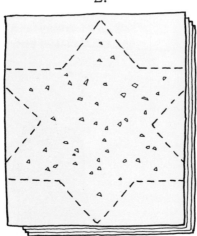

Did you know?

People first started sending each other Christmas cards in the 1840s, soon after the "Penny post" was started in England. Before then, it cost far too much money to send greetings to friends who lived far away.

You can make letter-cards in other Christmas shapes, such as bells or angels.

The Christmas Tree

Over a thousand years ago a Christian monk called Boniface went to Germany. One December night as he walked through a wood he saw some people who were going to sacrifice a boy to their god, Odin. They had the boy tied to an oak tree. Boniface cut down the oak tree before the boy could be harmed. In the ground between the roots of the oak tree was a small fir tree. Boniface used the event to tell the people about the love of God and his promise to give eternal life to people. He gave the little fir tree to them as a sign of eternal life, as its leaves were always green. So began the tradition of the Christmas tree.

Little Christmas trees

WHAT YOU NEED

★ stiff paper or thin card

★ green and brown paint

★ glue

★ scissors

1. Fold a piece of card and draw half a Christmas tree, with the centre line on the fold. Cut it out.

2. Open out your Christmas tree shape and draw round the outline three times. Cut out these three pieces.

Paint the green leaves and brown stump.

3. Fold each piece down the centre, and then glue them back to back.

Use the same method to make other shapes, such as bells and lanterns. If you make small decorations in this way and add a thread loop, you can hang them on a real Christmas tree.

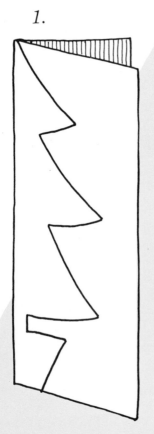

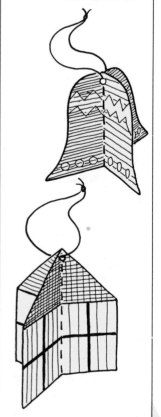

Christmas tree cookies

Hang these cookies on the tree. They will look very pretty. But don't forget to ask some friends round to eat them up while they are still fresh!

WHAT YOU NEED

★ 225g/8oz plain flour
★ 1 teaspoon cinnamon
★ 75g/3oz butter
★ 75g/3oz sugar
★ 1 egg
★ bowl
★ rolling pin
★ cookie cutters or knife
★ baking tray lined with baking parchment
★ wire rack
★ drinking straw
★ icing sugar
★ cake decorations, such as silver balls and sugar strands
★ silver or gold thread, or thin wool

1. Ask a grown-up to heat the oven to 180°C.

2. Mix the flour and cinnamon together in a bowl.

3. Work in the butter with your fingers until the mixture is crumbly.

4. Add the sugar and mix well.

5. Add the egg and stir to make a lump of dough.

6. Sprinkle a little extra flour on a clean work surface and on the rolling pin. Roll out the dough to about 5mm thickness.

7. Cut out shapes with cookie cutters or a knife and place each carefully on the baking tray. You can gather up the scraps of dough, knead them together and roll it out again until all the dough is used up.

8. Use the drinking straw like a cookie cutter to cut a little hole in each cookie about 1cm from the edge.

9. Ask a grown-up to help you bake the cookies for about 12 minutes, or until lightly brown. When they are cool enough to handle, spread them on the wire rack until they are quite cold.

10. Wash out your bowl. Mix some icing sugar with a very little water until you have a thick paste, about as thick as toothpaste. Use the icing and the cake decorations to decorate your cookies.

11. When the icing has set, thread a loop of thread through the hole in each and tie to the Christmas tree.

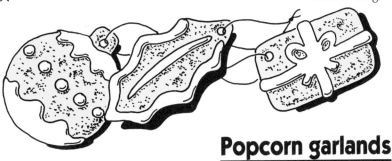

Popcorn garlands

WHAT YOU NEED

★ popping corn
★ large saucepan
★ butter
★ thick needle and fine string

1. Ask a grown-up to melt the butter in the large pan. Add the popping corn and put the lid on.

2. When you hear the corn begin to pop, ask the grown-up to shake the pan gently so that the corn does not burn. The corn will pop for a few minutes. When it has finished, remove the lid and leave to cool.

3. Thread your needle. Make a knot at the end of your string, and thread the popcorn on it. Make long strings that you can hang round the Christmas tree.

Later you can hang the popcorn garlands outside for the birds to eat.

All Wrapped Up

Part of the fun of Christmas is choosing and giving gifts. At Christmas time, the shops are overflowing with pretty things that no one needs or really wants. To choose a good gift, think about what a person really likes to do, and try to think of what they might need for those activities. It might be something quite plain, such as a mixing spoon for someone who likes cooking, or a set of flowerpots for someone who likes gardening. Then you can make it seem special by wrapping it up.

To make your own wrapping paper, you will need a supply of large sheets of white paper to print on, and scrap paper such as newspapers to protect the area where you are working from splashes.

Stencilled paper

WHAT YOU NEED

★ white paper to print on

★ smaller pieces of white paper

★ scissors

★ adhesive putty

★ small pieces of sponge

★ poster paints

1. Cut the smaller pieces of paper into circles, the size you want your snowflakes to be.

2. Fold the circles in half and half again. Cut out shapes along the folded edges. Unfold the paper to see your "snow-flakes". Select the ones you like best.

3. Lay a snowflake on the white wrapping paper, with tiny pieces of adhesive putty spaced around the edge to hold it in place. Dip the end of your sponge in paint. Squeeze out the excess. Dab the paint over the snowflake. Use the snowflakes in different positions until you have decorated the entire sheet of paper with snowflake stencils.

One way to make a gift look really special is to cut stencils to fit the wrapping exactly. First, you wrap the gift in plain paper. Then cut stencils to fit the main "panels" of the wrapped present.

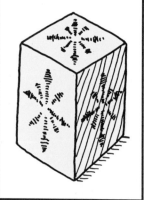

1.

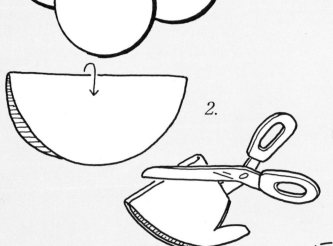

2.

3.

Gift bags

Some presents are a difficult shape to wrap. Others are soft and, however hard you try, the wrapped gift looks dismal and lumpy. A gift that is a special shape needs to be disguised, so the person receiving it can't guess what it is. You can solve all these problems by making gift bags. Then you simply slip the gift inside.

WHAT YOU NEED

★ a sheet of wrapping paper, large enough to fit easily round the gift

★ paper punch

★ sticky tape

★ wool or string

1. Fold the paper so that it meets in the centre as shown. Tape.

2. Fold up the end, turning in the corners as shown. Tape.

3. Mark the position of the holes for the string. Put a little piece of tape on the inside at these points to strengthen the holes.

Punch the holes, and thread wool or string through to make a handle.

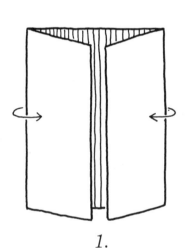

1.

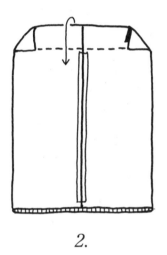

2.

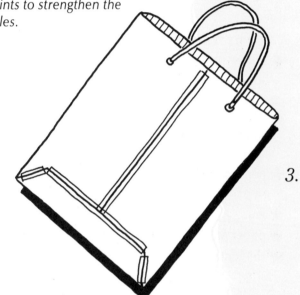

3.

Printed wrapping paper

WHAT YOU NEED

★ white paper to print on

★ potato

★ sharp knife

★ pen

★ poster paints

1. Cut the potato in half. Draw a simple design on the flat side, such as a star or a bell. Ask a grown-up to help you cut round the design, and then cut the rest of the potato surface away as shown.

2. Dip the design in paint and print carefully on to the paper. Arrange the motifs in an interesting pattern.

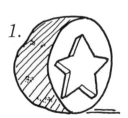

1.

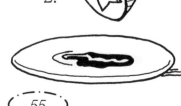

2.

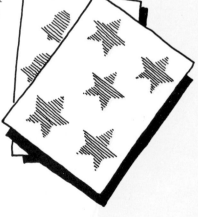

Sing for Joy

Carols are happy songs that are full of praise. There are carols for Christmas, Easter and Whitsun, but today the Christmas carols are the best known. Carollers used to dance in a ring as they sang, telling the story of what God had done for people. Do you know any carols that make you feel happy when you sing them? Why not make a carol book with all your favourite songs?

Make your own carol book

WHAT YOU NEED

★ coloured card, the size of your finished book

★ white paper, cut 3cm smaller all round than the card

★ pen, paper and crayons

★ glue

★ paper punch

★ thin cord

1. Think of a picture you could draw that illustrates your carol. Decide how it will fit on the page with your picture. Draw the picture on white paper and write in the carol.

2. Glue the carol in the centre of the card.

3. Glue your next carol on the back. Make several cards in this way.

4. Make a front cover for your book. Think of a title that expresses what these carols mean for you, and a picture to suit. Draw and write the cover.

5. Arrange the cards in a block in the order you want, with the cover on top and a blank card for the back. Punch a hole through them on the left edge.

6. Tie the cards together loosely with cord.

Why not get together with some friends to sing carols? Use your book to remind you of the words.

While shepherds watched their flocks by night,
    All seated on the ground,
    The angel of the Lord came down,
    And glory shone around.

"Fear not," said he, (for mighty dread
    Had seized their troubled mind),
    "Glad tidings of great joy I bring
    To you and all mankind.

"To you in David's town this day
    Is born of David's line
    A saviour, who is Christ the Lord;
    And this shall be the sign:

"The heavenly babe you there shall find
    To human view displayed,
    All meanly wrapped in swathing bands,
    And in a manger laid."

Nahum Tate (1652–1715)

Away in a manger, no crib for a bed,
    The little Lord Jesus laid down his sweet head;
    The stars in the bright sky looked down where he lay,
    The little Lord Jesus asleep on the hay.

The cattle are lowing, the baby awakes,
    But little Lord Jesus no crying he makes;
    I love thee, Lord Jesus: look down from the sky
    And stay by my side until morning is nigh.

Be near me, Lord Jesus: I ask thee to stay
    Close by me for ever and love me I pray;
    Bless all the dear children in thy tender care,
    And fit us for heaven, to live with thee there.

verses 1 and 2: anonymous (19th century)
verse 3: J.T. MacFarland (1906)

Christmas Day

Christmas Day is a special time for families. Often, someone in the family will cook a special meal and organize a family party. It is a time to make everyone welcome: a time for sharing. Here are some ideas you can use to make the party table look really festive and welcoming.

Star place mats

WHAT YOU NEED
★ stiff paper, about 20cm by 40cm
★ scissors
★ ruler
★ pencil

1. Cut two triangles with all their sides 20cm long. Draw a line 3.5cm up from the middle of the base of each triangle. Cut carefully along this line.

2. Join them together to make the place mat.

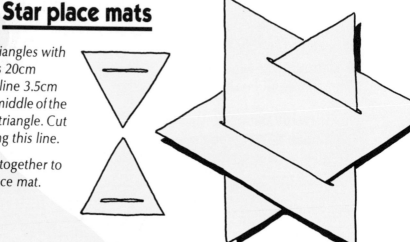

Serviette holder

It is traditional in some countries to hang stockings at Christmas. Then they are filled with gifts. The story is that, many years ago, there was a good man named Nicholas who gave gifts to poor people. He tried to do so without their knowing who had given the gift. One day, he climbed on to the roof of a house and dropped gold coins down the chimney. They landed in some stockings that were drying by the fire.

WHAT YOU NEED
★ scissors
★ stiff paper, about 30cm by 20cm
★ glue
★ crayons

1. Cut two stocking shapes out of stiff paper.

2. Glue the edges together but leave the top open.

3. Pattern the stocking brightly and add a name at the top.

4. Fold the serviette to fit the stocking.

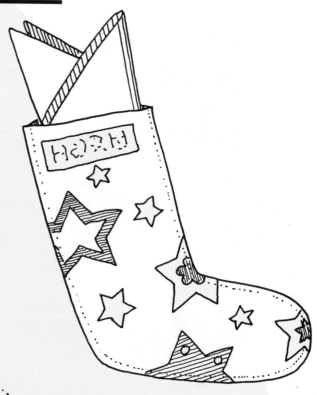

Table decoration

Collect together some evergreens, and perhaps some twigs with bright berries on them. Find an old plastic pot or container, and cover it with Christmas paper. Arrange your evergreens in the bowl with damp sand or flower foam to hold them in place. Decorate your arrangement with fir cones and red ribbon bows. You can use twist ties to hold these in place.

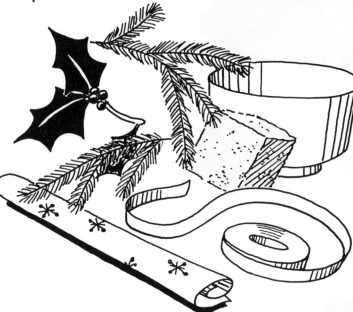

Festive napkin rings

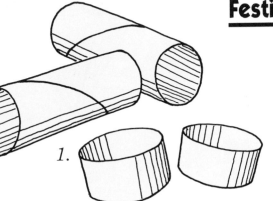

1.

WHAT YOU NEED

★ cardboard tube
★ foil or patterned paper
★ scissors
★ sticky tape

1. Cut the tube into 2.5cm lengths.

2. Cut the paper into rectangles 5cm wide, to fit round the tube sections. Centre the tube on the paper, roll the paper round and tape in place.

3. Snip the paper in several places and tuck inside. Tape if necessary.

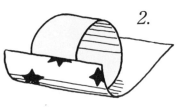

2.

3.

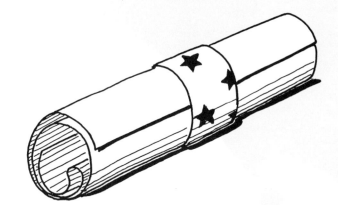

Goodbye Christmas

Christmas celebrations can't go on forever. In the Christian calendar, 6 January marks the end of Christmas. At this time, it is traditional to take down all the decorations. But don't just throw them away. You can save many things and be well ahead with your preparations for the next Christmas!

Gift cones

You can either make these now or just cut the semicircles and leave them flat till next Christmas.

WHAT YOU NEED

★ large Christmas cards

★ compasses and pencil, or a selection of round plates

★ scissors

★ sticky tape or staples

★ paper punch

★ wool or cord

1. Place the point of your compasses at the centre point on the fold of the Christmas card, and draw the largest semicircle that you can on the picture side. Or you can use a plate to help you draw a semicircle. Cut it out neatly with your scissors.

2. Roll it into a cone, and fasten with sticky tape or staples. Punch a hole on either side, and thread with wool or cord.

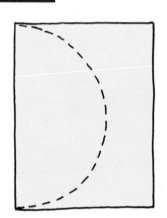

Next Christmas, you can hang these on the tree as decorations. You can fill these cones with tiny gifts, and hide them with a little crumpled tissue paper, to give to visitors.

Gift tags

WHAT YOU NEED

★ old Christmas cards

★ scissors

★ paper punch

★ wool

1. Select a pretty part of a Christmas card. Cut it out neatly.

2. Punch a hole at one end, trying not to spoil the design. Cut a length of wool and fold it in half. Thread the fold through the hole, and loop the ends through.

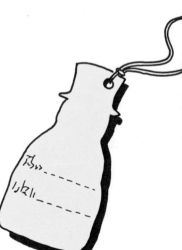

Christmas scrapbook

Every family has its own Christmas traditions. Keep a record of your Christmas in your own scrapbook.

★ *Write a menu of what you ate.*

★ *Ask all the people who came to sign their names. Ask them to give their ages too.*

★ *Collect pictures of everyone. If you don't have a camera, play a game in which everybody draws a picture of someone else, and put the pictures in your scrapbook.*

★ *Glue in pretty things that will remind you of Christmas.*

★ *Staple your pages together.*

★ *Make the cover bright with scraps of wrapping paper.*

★ *Put the year on your scrapbook.*

If there is someone in your family who can't be with you at Christmas, make a scrapbook card to send them.

Did you know?

On 6 January many Christians celebrate the arrival of the wise men, who brought gifts to the baby Jesus. In some countries people give and receive gifts on this day.

Index of Activities

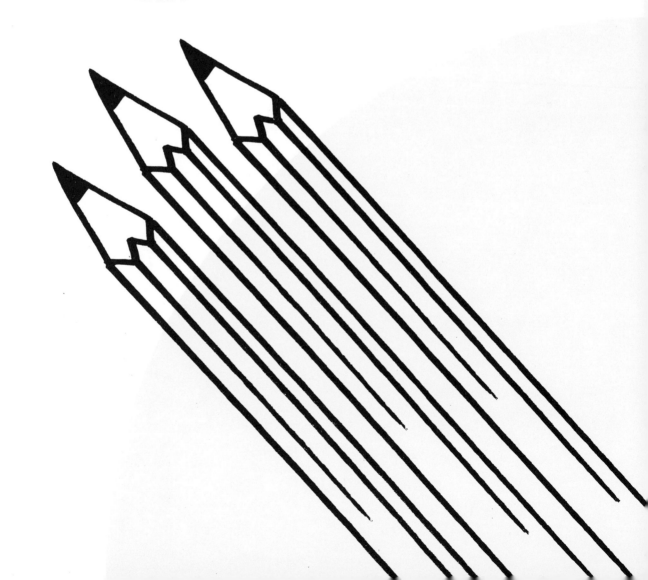